I.S.B.N. 0 85079 122 7

SUNDAY EXPRESS & DAILY EXPRESS
CARTOONS

Thirty-sixth Series

AN EXPRESS BOOKS PUBLICATION

© 1982 Express Newspapers Limited, Fleet Street, London EC4P 4JT

Printed in Great Britain by Purnell and Sons (Book Production) Ltd., Paulton, Bristol

£1.50

INTRODUCTION

by

TERRY

WOGAN

Well known Radio and Television personality

I first met Carl Giles (I throw the "Carl" in there, to indicate our familiarity, nay, intimacy. Frankly, until our introduction, I always thought he was Giles Somebody or Other, didn't you?) at a "Saints and Sinners Dinner" at The Savoy, London. And, no, The Orpheans were *not* playing. I'm too young for them, and Giles denies all knowledge. . . . Actually, its the *only* time I've met this silvery-haired artist and bon viveur. He greeted me in that manly, almost rough way of his, and after I'd picked myself up from the floor, he was kindness itself to a simple lad, untutored in the gentry's smart ways. He hardly spilled any drink over me at all, and even showed me how to remove white wine stains with red wine. I've got another shirt now, anyway. . . .

In the course of this fateful evening, in a moment of weakness, Giles asked me to write this introduction. He regrets it now, of course, but its far too late. Like the rest of you, I've admired the man's brilliance for too long to let an opportunity like this go by. There's more going on in a darkened corner of a Giles cartoon than most other artists achieve in a lifetime. I'd compare him with Rembrandt, if I wasn't afraid I'd meet him again. . . .

"I told her it's at St. Paul's but she says they always have 'em here"

Daily Express, July 29th, 1981

"I told him we wouldn't sing unless he paid us the same as St. Paul's Choir and all he said was 'Thanks'"

Sunday Express, July 19th, 1981

"You'll have to take if off Grandma—Butch doesn't like it!"

Sunday Express, July 26th, 1981

"Never mind the happy couple kissing in public—you two knock it off!"

Daily Express, August 1st, 1981

"Playing up 'ell because she couldn't find her woolly egg warmer on show"

Daily Express, August 6th, 1981

"George, do the SAS take on private rescue jobs?"

Sunday Express, August 9th, 1981

"If I was your Fred with an appointment on Monday about his contract
I wouldn't have clobbered the Chairman first ball"

Sunday Express, August 16th, 1981

"Taxi, Sir? Certainly, Sir"

Daily Express, August 20th, 1981

"I don't care how much petrol and telephoning it would save, your Sweetum's not moving in to live with us"

Sunday Express, August 23rd, 1981

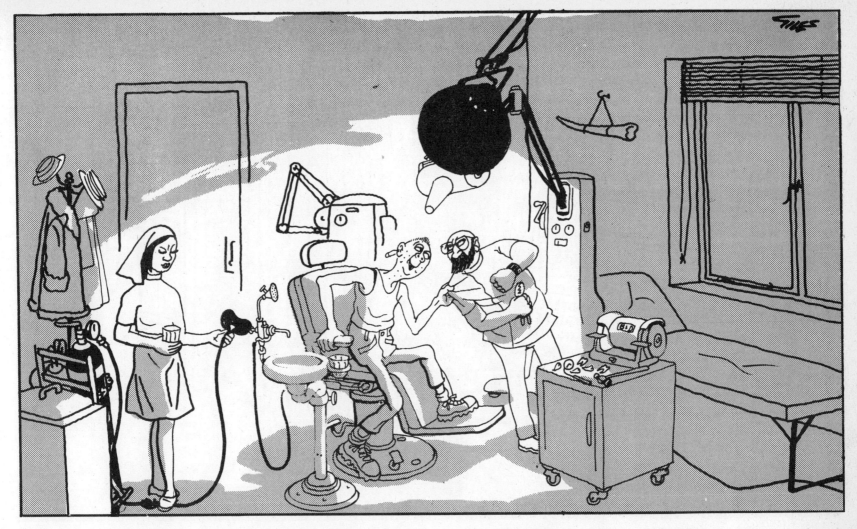

"I got a copper fined £40 for clipping me ear, me teacher fined £50 for kicking me backside—
so if you give me as much as one little twinge, boyo . . ."

Daily Express, August 25th, 1981

"I know I hate cricket as much as you do—I only said I was THINKING of taking it up"

Daily Express, August 27th, 1981

"Thanks to your witty 'Here comes Sebastian Coe' he's now serving everybody else first"

Sunday Express, August 30th, 1981

"Poor Penelope—she thought they were going back THIS Tuesday"

Daily Express, September 1st, 1981

"We'll have to stop him breaking these speed records before breakfast"

Daily Express, September 3rd, 1981

"There you are darling—Prince Charles had chicken-pox and HE grew up to be a fine big boy"

(Royal medical secrets dumped on tip)

Sunday Express, September 6th, 1981

"Here we are Vera, 'Last date for posting Christmas cards overland to Zambia, Barindi,
Chile, Rwanda and Uganda—Monday"

Daily Express, September 10th, 1981

"And we all know who'll be tidying up after that episcopal porker—Mrs. Archbishop of Canterbury"

Sunday Express, September 13th, 1981

"My father says none of you've got a cat's chance in hell of being a Lloyd George"

Daily Express, September 15th, 1981

"Burwood, would a note to your father persuade him to keep you at home for about six years?"

(Boy plays truant for six years)

Daily Express, September 17th, 1981

"What special rights has Roy Jenkins got to stop the non-stop London Express that my sister Millie hasn't got?"

(Express train makes special stop to pick up Roy Jenkins)

Sunday Express, September 20th, 1981

"There are plenty of jobs going if you'd bother to look for them—Arts Council Grant
£800 for picture to show what life's like in a pub!"

Daily Express, September 22nd, 1981

"I didn't bring over 14 bodyguards for Clint Eastwood to use for target practice!"

Daily Express, September 24th, 1981

"Everybody in the canteen expects Lord Nelson to do his duty and buy them a drink, M'Lord"

Daily Express, September 29th, 1981

"He found Skegness so bracing he's decided to come back to stay with his family"

(Visiting walrus returned to Artic from Skegness)

Sunday Express, October 4th, 1981

"Shirley Williams? I've got just the person—you'll be so glad to get out of the house you'll be on the platform before the train leaves the depot"

Daily Express, October 6th, 1981

"It's a hard world—no sooner do they ban footballers kissing than they bring in women refs"

Sunday Express, October 11th, 1981

"Here's something to remove burdens from your anxious minds, bid your hopes to be confirmed, urge the inactive into battle, teach accomplishments—Honiton beat Ashton at conkers"

Daily Express, October 13th, 1981

"Nice try, but I don't think your boy will bring in the cash like a new panda"

Daily Express, October 15th, 1981

"When it comes to stubborn, pig-headed iron ladies—we've got our built-in model T"

Sunday Express, October 18th, 1981

"I reckon she heard you say 'Hear, hear' to Ted's speech at Blackpool"

Daily Express, October 20th, 1981

"Here comes one—trip him up and start 'ollering 'RAPE!'"

Sunday Express, October 25th, 1981

"14 extra cups of tea for the National Consumer Council come to watch this cowboy put a washer on the tap"

(National Consumer Council to inspect workers in action)

Daily Express, October 27th, 1981

"Dad, why hasn't that lady got any . . . ?"

Daily Express, October 29th, 1981

"That Woodhouse woman's raving mad teaching children to feed horses
sugar with their mouths—your boy has just bitten my Hercules!"

Sunday Express, November 1st, 1981

"No, this is not your very own cuddly Peterkins. This is his very own cuddly wifeykins!"

Daily Express, November 3rd, 1981

"How do you keep fireworks away from a pet who's just eaten all your Atomic Bangers?"

Daily Express, November 5th, 1981

"I suppose one could say you were a sort of demonstration missile when your Haig sent you to the Somme, Grandfather"

Sunday Express, November 8th, 1981

"We demand police protection from independent bodies taking pictures of us at work"

(Gang captured by secret camera)

Daily Express, November 10th, 1981

"That's the third bout of nervous tension you've had this month"

Daily Express, November 12th, 1981

"Sotheby's said Prince Philip's painting would benefit from a course in life studies"

Sunday Express, November 15th, 1981

"You come a McEnroe with me and I'll maim yer"

Daily Express, November 17th, 1981

"Morning, Froid—we hear you're the only boy who did his homework instead of watching football last night"

Daily Express, November 19th, 1981

"I not leave Espana for Francisco Franco—I not leave Espana for British football riff-raff!"

Sunday Express, November 22nd, 1981

"Dad, you know the Consumers Association said a goose is a better guard dog than a dog?"

Daily Express, November 24th, 1981

"Don't go away son—me and my mate are just going to have consultation whether we thump your head or kick your backside"

Daily Express, November 26th, 1981

"Good evening, Mrs. Sykes. I'm searching for a member of my flock
who hath gone astray—a rather well-fed turkey, to be precise"

Sunday Express, November 29th, 1981

"His bloody horse takes home more on a Friday than I do!"

Daily Express, December 1st, 1981

"Grandma—stop saying over and over 'I'm not paying £46 for that!' YOU don't pay anything for that"

Daily Express, December 3rd, 1981

"If your dinner's late blame Mrs. Thatcher—she started this on TV"

(Mrs. Thatcher leads children in physical jerks)

Sunday Express, December 6th, 1981

"Sorry to keep you waiting, M'lady — they're judging this gentleman's sheep at Smithfield this afternoon"

Daily Express, December 8th, 1981

"Nice one, Luv—get off the train and walk the rest of the way to Waterloo—you know the way"

(Snowbound commuters take to the tracks)

Daily Express, December 10th, 1981

"You say your mate kept saying 'Innit pretty?' So you braked
hard with the intention of causing him grievous bodily harm"

Sunday Express, December 13th, 1981

"Stanley! There's a lady says her Christmas tree lights have gone out"

Daily Express, December 15th, 1981

"When I ask 'Who's been sleeping in my bed?' I don't expect damn fool answers like 'The Queen'"

(Queen snowbound in small hotel)

Daily Express, December 17th, 1981

"Betting on how many times Albert goes head over tip between the barn and the stables is
not the same as a day at Kempton"

Sunday Express, December 20th, 1981

"I think I should put a coat on, Celia, even if it does crumple your dress for the office party"

Daily Express, December 22nd, 1981

"Rejoice good Christian men—the group's arrived"

Daily Express, December 24th, 1981

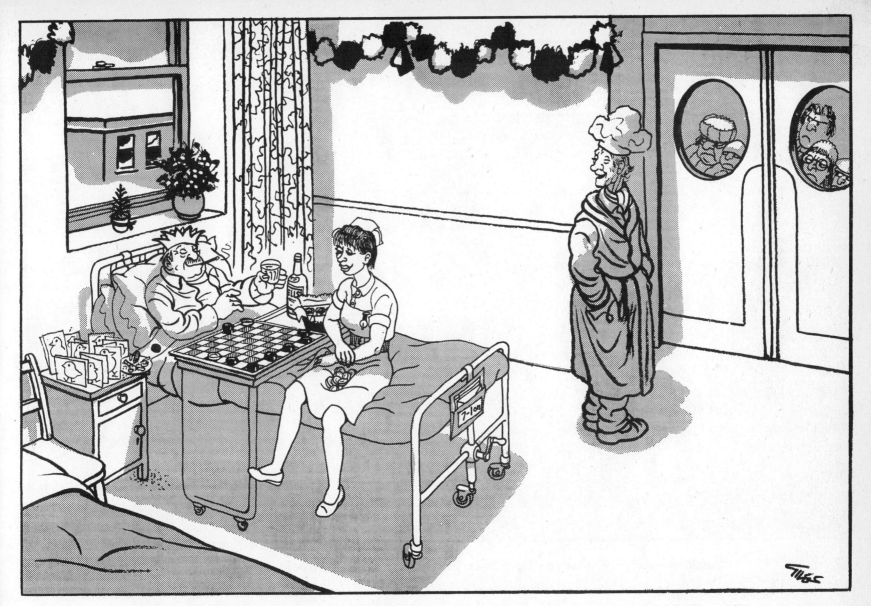

"You were saying, Harry, about it being heaven to be in here away from the wife and family for a bit"

Sunday Express, December 27th, 1981

"Geraldine, remember that joke foam brick you threw at the Chairman at the office party?"

Daily Express, December 29th, 1981

"Look, sonny—we've had enough hoax bear stories for one year—so get your stuffed gorilla out of here"

Daily Express, December 31st, 1981

"Who's going to volunteer to tell Grandma the delivery strike's been called off but Butch has eaten her Bingo page?"

Sunday Express, January 3rd, 1982

"Jimmy Savile says it can't be fixed, so we'll have to buy a new one. I smell a fiddle!"

Daily Express, January 7th, 1982

"No problem—he'll come out in the Land Rover and tow you home—only eight miles from here, you said?"

Sunday Express, January 10th, 1982

"Before you start—do you mind getting off my skis?"

Daily Express, January 12th, 1982

"Dad! You've won a smashing family Speed Boat—can I tell Mum?"

Sunday Express, January 17th, 1982

"He's scared to take one of his coats off and roll his sleeves up in case you have him for streaking"

Daily Express, January 19th, 1982

"I want you all to go out and restore our image—and you, Wilson, keep your hat on at all times"

Daily Express, January 21st, 1982

"Typical ain't it! When you really need a copper you can never find one"

Sunday Express, July 12th, 1981

"Louis's mummy would like you outside for three-minute rounds"

(Magistrate tells teachers to expect to be hit)

Sunday Express, January 24th, 1982

"Liz—you know there's a meeting at ten—did you remember to wake Willie?"

Daily Express, January 28th, 1982

"Didn't Dad have funny little legs when he was a Scout"

Sunday Express, January 31st, 1982

"Come and have a look at one of the bloodthirsty hunting junkies—as Spike Milligan calls 'em"

Daily Express, February 2nd, 1982

"Why'd you tell Auntie Bertha we can't come for the weekend because there are no trains?
She only lives four doors up"

Daily Express, February 4th, 1982

"They said that about my parents? That's good for a £100,000 libel!"

(Footballer wins £100,000 libel)

Sunday Express, February 7th, 1982

"Get him off my chair"

Daily Express, February 11th, 1982

"The Valentines Grandma sent to Ray Buckton and Sir Peter Parker—they're charging her for sending obscene literature through the post"

Sunday Express, February 14th, 1982

"Sorry I kept you waiting, sir—I heard we'd gone back to work so I shut 'em"

Daily Express, February 18th, 1982

"You had better listen to this—there's a clause in this Government grant
that says something about increased productivity"

Sunday Express, February 21st, 1982

"Teacher says he blames the parents and told me to give you six of the best—ONE . . . !"

Sunday Express, February 28th, 1982

"Your eggs are done, dear—they're on father's head"

Daily Express, March 4th, 1982

"Ah, Kerridge, still wearing the old patriotic camouflage you wore on your midnight reconnoitres among my pheasants during the last lot?"

Sunday Express, March 7th, 1982

"Lord, whatever he taxes, please let him tax all transistor radios out of existence"

Daily Express, March 9th, 1982

"The wheels of the economy sure turn in a mysterious way—my 6% wage increase
just pays for his 9p a gallon increase"

Daily Express, March 11th, 1982

"It looks fishy to me—two wardens buying a new car the day parking fines go up to £10"

Sunday Express, March 14th, 1982

"Most jobs in industry will always call for male superior strength and stamina"

Daily Express, March 16th, 1982

"This must be the most burglar-proof house in the district.
My boy won't let me in because I've forgotten the password"

Daily Express, March 18th, 1982

"Here come three of my good reasons for bringing back hanging"

Sunday Express, March 21st, 1982

"Tell your little friend Singh to take them back to the Indian Festival right now!"

Daily Express, March 23rd, 1982

"I love the start of the Flat—all of 'em been stuffing themselves for three months in Barbados"

Daily Express, March 25th, 1982

"Mind the new lawnmower—dad couldn't decide between a ride on air-cushioned or cylinder type"

Sunday Express, March 28th, 1982

"Those woollies you sent for the Royal Baby—they've sent them back"

Daily Express, March 30th, 1982

"Vera, I think you've been doing a bit too much of this Daily Express F-slimming plan!"

Daily Express, May 18th, 1982

CAME A NEW WAR. . . .

"But when the blast of war blows in our ears . . . Stiffen the sinews,
Summon up the blood . . . Clear out the old air-raid shelter . . ."

Sunday Express, April 4th, 1982

"Maggie will have to send us some live ammo if she wants to see another Cowes Week under British rule"

Daily Express, April 6th, 1982

"Here she comes—will we take back 200 tins of Argentine corned beef she's been hoarding since Suez?"

Daily Express, April 8th, 1982

"You'll have to make your mind up quick, Sir—I've had an offer from the Government and the Argentinians"

Sunday Express, April 11th, 1982

"At least we know now that the Falkland Islands are not the ones north of the Hebrides and the Orkneys are not somewhere off South America"

Daily Express, April 13th, 1982

"The U.S. Secretary of State has been to Argentina and back three or four times since I ordered my egg and chips"

Daily Express, April 15th, 1982

"Uncle Rodney's getting in early with his memoirs of the Battle of the Falklands"

Sunday Express, April 18th, 1982

"Out come the old '39-'45 war jokes—'If you want to help our boys you should send those socks to the enemy'"

Sunday Express, April 25th, 1982

"Nothing in the post but the usual bills, oh, and a white feather from
the lady you were discussing the Falkland war with"

Daily Express, April 27th, 1982

"Tell the Honourable Gentlemen the War Cabinet is about to adjourn for the day"

Daily Express, April 29th, 1982

"Off you go and rejoice—and steer clear of the Falklands 200 mile restricted zone"

Daily Express, May 2nd, 1982

"Unconfirmed report that one of your jump-jets has made a direct hit on Dad's cornflakes"

Daily Express, May 4th, 1982

"Psst! It's upside down"

Daily Express, May 11th, 1982

"If you'd sent your Grandma on holiday to Buenos Aires two months ago there wouldn't be a Junta now"

Sunday Express, May 23rd, 1982

"Call dad and remind him he arranged last night to go on the Great Marathon Race this morning"

Sunday Express, May 9th, 1982

"Oh boy! These two are mine—one civil servant at 14.3%, and one judge at 18.6% wage increase!"

Sunday Express, May 16th, 1982

"What d'you mean you've melted them all down into Father Christmases already? He's coming after all!"

Daily Express, May 27th, 1982

"Reminding daddy that the Pope can pack Wembley with a crowd as big
as the Cup Final does nothing for Christian Unity, Prunella"

*unday Express, May 30th, 1982

"That day off I gave you to go and see the Pope . . . He's in Scotland"

Daily Express, June 1st, 1982

"Advance posse from the President—bodyguard to Two-gun Liz, Terror of Windsor Gulch"

(President demands bodyguard for visit to Windsor)

nday Express, June 6th, 1982

"Knock it off, Drummond, President Reagan's gone"

Daily Express, June 10th, 1982

"That Spanish ticket fella who told us to 'Wait in here a minute . . .'"

Sunday Express, June 13th, 1982

"Room service has gone way down hill since we beat the Argentinians"

Daily Express, June 17th, 1982

"Awake my love, 'tis Father's Day—for a special treat you've got football all the afternoon on TV"

Sunday Express, June 20th, 1982

"Three months Northern Ireland, 11 weeks Falklands, now report for
crowd control outside St. Mary's Hospital!"

(It's a boy! Prince William arrives)

Daily Express, June 22nd, 1982

"Mummy! His Royal Highness wants changing again"

Daily Express, June 24th, 1982

"Dad's back from his trial run for getting to work tomorrow"

(Another rail strike threat)

Sunday Express, June 27th, 1982

"I don't think madam appreciated your little joke, offering her a broom as alternative transport"

Daily Express, June 29th, 1982

"Don't rush back from the pub—I'm doing the washing instead of cooking dinner—flexible rostering"

Sunday Express, July 4th, 1982

"You walked from one end of the Falklands to the other—so what's so bad
about walking from Southampton to Glasgow?"

Daily Express, July 8th, 1982

"He's been confined to the car for butting in with 'Sid Weighell's a goodun' when Auntie Bertha was running on about Union bosses"

Sunday Express, July 18th, 1982

"Now don't forget it's off to work by train today . . . don't hit the engine driver, and don't catch anything off the seats while the nurses are on strike"

Daily Express, July 20th, 1982